The naughty kitten

by Frances Kendle

Illustrated by Angela Mills

Brimax · Newmarket · England

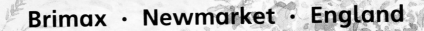

Ching and Chang are two Siamese kittens who love exploring the garden. Everything has to be sniffed and anything that moves has to be chased. The trouble is that Chang is always getting into mischief.

Hardly a day goes by when he does not do something naughty. But because they look so much alike, Chang makes sure it is Ching who gets the blame. One afternoon, after taking a nap, Chang leaps out of their basket.

"Come on Ching," he says excitedly. "Let's go and have some fun."

"I'm not going out anymore," says Ching. "I had to go without my cream at lunchtime because of you."

"Please yourself," says Chang, and he scampers off.

Ching curls up and tries to get back to sleep, but he cannot so he sets off to find his brother. To his surprise Chang is sitting quietly beside the garden pond washing his face. For once he is behaving himself.

Ching hurries to join him. As he draws nearer, he sees something that makes his fur stand on end. A glance in the pond and Ching's fears are confirmed. Oscar's ball is in the pond! Oscar is a big dog who lives in the same house as the kittens, but he does not like them one little bit. The ball in the pond is the thing Oscar loves most in the world.

"Ch . . Ch . . Chang," Ching stammers. "What have you done?" Chang stops washing and glances innocently at his shaking brother. "What is the matter? I have not done anything," he replies. Ching looks again at the pond.

"But you have," Ching insists. "Oscar's ball is in the pond," he says in horror.

"What ball?" says crafty Chang. "I have not seen any ball," he grins. Then he shoots off and hides in the bushes.

Poor Ching is so worried about getting the blame that he feels like running away and never coming back. He gazes in despair at the pond, he does not know what to do. Then suddenly he has an idea. Ching knows that his brother is a very good swimmer and he decides to play a trick on him.

"Chang! Chang! Come quickly!" he bellows. "There is something horrible in our pond!" Ching knows that his brother is not only naughty but very nosey as well. Almost at once Chang leaves his hiding place and bounds across the grass to look.

"Where?" he shouts and stares excitedly into the water. "Right near the edge," says Ching pretending to be afraid. Chang walks over to the edge of the pond and stoops for a closer look. Ching lifts his paw and gives him a shove. SPLASH! Chang falls into the water. A very wet and a very angry Chang climbs out of the pond.

The sight of his soaking wet
brother makes Ching roar with
laughter. A water lily is
stuck to his head and weeds
are hanging around his neck
and tripping him up as he walks.
"Oh dear!" laughs Ching, who
by now is lying on the grass
with his feet in the air.
Chang is very angry.

"What did you do that for?" he shouts.

"Well, Oscar's ball is in the water," says Ching.

"I know that. It fell in while I was playing with it," says Chang angrily.

"I know," Ching chuckles, "but as the ball is in the water and you are the kitten who is wet, this time you will get the blame."

Chang realises how clever his brother has been.

"So there is not anything horrible in the pond after all?" he asks.

"Not now", says Ching. "It just crawled out!" and taking to his heels he disappears behind the garden shed.

Say these words again

angry	mischief
afraid	scampers
surprise	naughty
something	horror
replies	suddenly
nosey	bounds